Take a Chance

Britannica

ENCYCLOPÆDIA BRITANNICA EDUCATIONAL CORPORATION

Mathematics in Context is a comprehensive curriculum for the middle grades. It was developed in collaboration with the Wisconsin Center for Education Research, School of Education, University of Wisconsin–Madison and the Freudenthal Institute at the University of Utrecht, The Netherlands, with the support of National Science Foundation Grant No. 9054928.

National Science Foundation

Opinions expressed are those of the authors
and not necessarily those of the Foundation

ISBN 0-7826-1507-4
1 2 3 4 5 6 7 8 9 10 99 98 97

The *Mathematics in Context* Development Team

Mathematics in Context is a comprehensive curriculum for the middle grades. The National Science Foundation funded the National Center for Research in Mathematical Sciences Education at the University of Wisconsin–Madison to develop and field test the materials from 1991 through 1996. The Freudenthal Institute at the University of Utrecht in The Netherlands, as a subcontractor, collaborated with the University of Wisconsin–Madison on the development of the curriculum.

National Center for Research in Mathematical Sciences Education Staff

Thomas A. Romberg
Director

Joan Daniels Pedro
Assistant to the Director

Gail Burrill
Coordinator
Field Test Materials

Margaret Meyer
Coordinator
Pilot Test Materials

Mary Ann Fix
Editorial Coordinator

Sherian Foster
Editorial Coordinator

James A. Middleton
Pilot Test Coordinator

Project Staff

Jonathan Brendefur
Laura J. Brinker
James Browne
Jack Burrill
Rose Byrd
Peter Christiansen
Barbara Clarke
Doug Clarke
Beth R. Cole

Fae Dremock
Jasmina Milinkovic
Margaret A. Pligge
Mary C. Shafer
Julia A. Shew
Aaron N. Simon
Marvin Smith
Stephanie Z. Smith
Mary S. Spence

Freudenthal Institute Staff

Jan de Lange
Director

Els Feijs
Coordinator

Martin van Reeuwijk
Coordinator

Project Staff

Mieke Abels
Nina Boswinkel
Frans van Galen
Koeno Gravemeijer
Marja van den Heuvel-Panhuizen
Jan Auke de Jong
Vincent Jonker
Ronald Keijzer

Martin Kindt
Jansie Niehaus
Nanda Querelle
Anton Roodhardt
Leen Streefland
Adri Treffers
Monica Wijers
Astrid de Wild

Table of Contents

Dear Student,

You are about to begin the study of the *Mathematics in Context* unit *Take a Chance*. Think about the following words and what they mean to you: *fair, sure, uncertain, not likely, impossible*. In this unit, you will see how these words are used in mathematics.

You will toss coins and number cubes and record the outcomes. Do you think you can predict how many times a head will come up if you toss a coin a certain number of times? Is the chance of getting a head greater than the chance of getting a tail? As you investigate these ideas, you are beginning the study of probability.

When several different things can happen, you will learn how to count all of the possibilities in a "smart" way. Keep alert during the next few weeks for statements that you may read or hear, such as "The chance of rain is 50%." You might even keep a record of such statements and bring them to share with the class.

We hope you enjoy learning about chance!

Sincerely,

The Mathematics in Context Development Team

This unit follows Hillary and Robert, students at Eagle School in Maine, as they experiment with using **chance** to make decisions.

You probably already know some things about chance.

1. What do you think of when someone says the word *chance*?

Choosing

Hillary and Robert both want to play *Super Math Wiz III*, a computer game, during lunch. The game is installed on one computer in the classroom. Since only one person can play at a time, Hillary and Robert have to decide who will play the game first.

2. How would you solve this problem in a ***fair*** way?

3. What do you think it means to be *fair*?

There are many situations in which you have to find a fair way to make a decision.

Robert says to Hillary, "If you throw a 6 with this number cube, you can play; otherwise, I'll play."

4. Do you think this is fair? Why or why not?

5. Can you come up with a better way to decide?

Hillary and Robert finally decide to use a spinner like the one on the left. They decide to spin once. If the arrow points to black, Hillary will go first. If the arrow points to white, Robert will go first.

6. Is this a fair method? Why or why not?

By now, everyone in Hillary's and Robert's class has heard about the computer game and wants to play. Hillary says, "Okay, okay! Let's put all of our names in a hat, and the person who is picked gets to play."

7. Is this fair? Why or why not?

A method for choosing is *fair* if it gives everyone the same chance of being chosen.

8. Think of two other situations in which it is important to be fair.

Fair Again

Hillary and Robert both want to play the computer game again the next day. They decide to toss a coin to see who will play first. Since there is an equal chance (sometimes called a 50-50 chance) of getting either heads or tails, this is a fair method.

You can draw a diagram with branches like a tree to show the two possibilities. The path you take on the tree shows the side of the coin that came up.

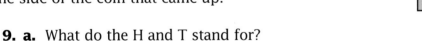

9. a. What do the H and T stand for?

   b. Robert says, "You know, the diagram shows that there's a 50-50 chance of getting a head or a tail." Explain what Robert means.

Look at a number cube.

10. a. How many different numbers can you roll on a number cube?

   b. Draw a picture to show the different possibilities.

11. How could Robert and Hillary use a number cube to decide in a fair way who will play the game first?

12. Hillary and Robert have a black-and-white cube. Hillary wins if it comes up white, and Robert wins if it comes up black. How can you tell if the cube has been colored in a fair way?

Activity

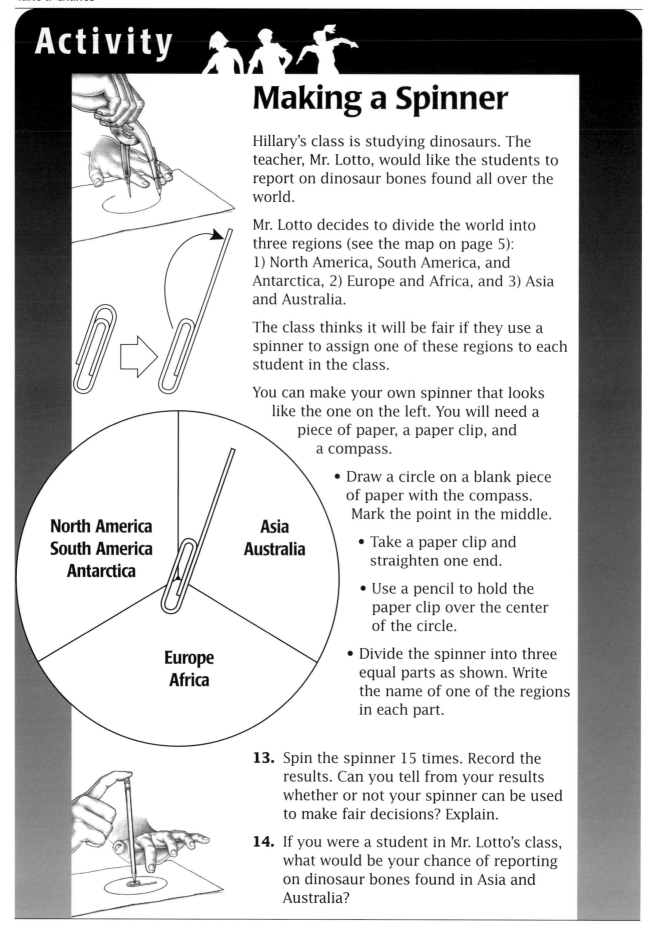

Making a Spinner

Hillary's class is studying dinosaurs. The teacher, Mr. Lotto, would like the students to report on dinosaur bones found all over the world.

Mr. Lotto decides to divide the world into three regions (see the map on page 5): 1) North America, South America, and Antarctica, 2) Europe and Africa, and 3) Asia and Australia.

The class thinks it will be fair if they use a spinner to assign one of these regions to each student in the class.

You can make your own spinner that looks like the one on the left. You will need a piece of paper, a paper clip, and a compass.

- Draw a circle on a blank piece of paper with the compass. Mark the point in the middle.
  - Take a paper clip and straighten one end.
  - Use a pencil to hold the paper clip over the center of the circle.
- Divide the spinner into three equal parts as shown. Write the name of one of the regions in each part.

North America South America Antarctica

Asia Australia

Europe Africa

13. Spin the spinner 15 times. Record the results. Can you tell from your results whether or not your spinner can be used to make fair decisions? Explain.

14. If you were a student in Mr. Lotto's class, what would be your chance of reporting on dinosaur bones found in Asia and Australia?

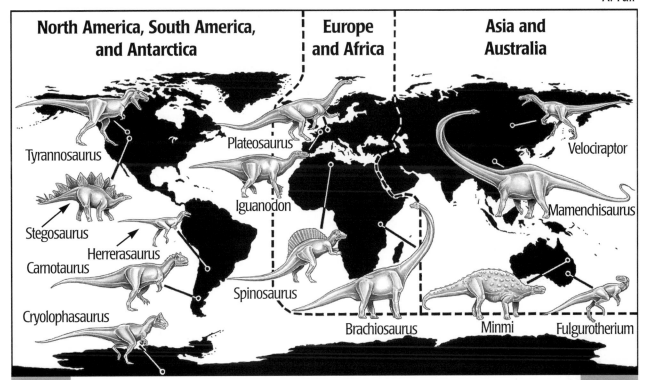

| North America, South America, and Antarctica | Europe and Africa | Asia and Australia |

Tyrannosaurus

Stegosaurus

Herrerasaurus

Carnotaurus

Cryolophasaurus

Plateosaurus

Iguanodon

Spinosaurus

Brachiosaurus

Velociraptor

Mamenchisaurus

Minmi

Fulgurotherium

Shanna wonders whether or not a spinner made out of a triangle can be used to make fair decisions.

15. a. Draw a triangle on paper. Can you make the triangle into a fair spinner?

 b. How can you tell whether it is fair or not?

 c. Can any triangle be made into a fair spinner? Support your answer with some examples.

16. a. Jonathan wonders if he can use a number cube to choose regions in a fair way. Can he? If so, how?

 b. Kara wonders if she can use a coin. Can she?

17. How can you tell whether or not a particular method will be fair? Explain your answer.

18. Since many bones were recently found in Europe and Africa, Mr. Lotto thinks there should be more students reporting on this region than on the other regions.

 a. How would you make a spinner so that the region "Europe and Africa" is picked more often?

 b. Would this spinner be fair?

Activity

Different Chance Objects

Hillary wonders whether or not objects other than spinners and number cubes can be used to make fair decisions. When objects are not shaped as regularly as coins, number cubes, or spinners, it can be hard to tell. One way to find out is to flip or spin the object over and over again to see what happens each time.

Your teacher will divide the class into groups. Each group will get one of the items listed below:

- a large paper cup
- a small paper cup
- a chalkboard eraser
- a bottle cap
- the spinner on the left

Your job is to find out whether or not you can use your item in any way to make a fair decision.

19. Throw or spin your item 30 times. Make a table of your results. When you are done, decide whether or not you can use your item to make a fair decision. Report your results to the class.

Note: Keep these results, because you will use them again later in the unit.

The Concert

Next week Compass Rose, a rock band that Hillary likes, is coming to play in Eagle. Hillary's mother got four tickets to the concert. She will take Hillary and two of her friends.

Unfortunately, Hillary has three friends she wants to bring and has to find a fair way to decide who will go with her.

20. Find a fair way to decide which two friends will go with Hillary. You may use coins, number cubes, spinners, or anything else you think may be fair.

Oh no! Another of Hillary's friends wants to go too!

21. Come up with a fair way to decide which two of the four will go with Hillary now.

22. Give your opinion about the fairness of each of the following situations:

   a. Two soccer teams toss a coin before a game to see which team gets to choose a goal.

   b. In Mr. Ryan's class, there are 10 boys and 15 girls. To decide who will be hall monitors each day, Mr. Ryan draws the name of one girl from a box holding all of the girls' names and the name of one boy from a box holding all of the boys' names.

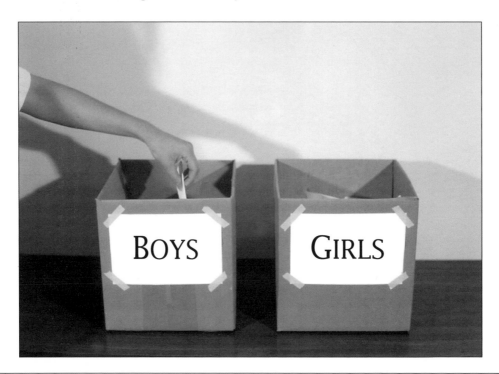

c. Only 50 students can go on a field trip to the zoo because there is only one bus. The principal decides to allow the first 50 who sign up before school in the morning to go on the trip.

d. In the United States, all people 18 years old or older are eligible to vote for a presidential candidate.

Summary

There are many situations in daily life that involve chance or in which you must make fair decisions. *Fair* means that every possibility has the same chance of occurring.

In order to make fair decisions, you should use a *fair* method. Typical things that can help you make fair decisions are coins, number cubes, and spinners. There are many other objects that can help you make fair decisions

Summary Questions

23. a. Can you toss a pencil to make a fair decision? How might you find out?

b. Can you toss a thumbtack to make a fair decision? How might you find out?

A quiz show on television features two teams from local schools that compete every week. A participating school may send 40 students to sit in the audience. The principal of Eagle School has decided that each of the eight classes in the school should select—by a drawing—five students who will go to the studio.

On the left is a list of the eight classes at Eagle School.

The principal says that her method is fair.

Class	Number of Students	Number Selected
Ms. Johnson	25	5
Mr. Geist	27	5
Ms. Lanie	32	5
Ms. McGill	31	5
Mr. Ford	24	5
Ms. Durden	25	5
Mr. Shore	29	5
Mr. Lane	32	5

24. a. If you were a student at Eagle School, which class would you want to be in?

b. Is the principal's method fair?

c. Hillary and Robert have decided to design a different method that will be fair for the principal to use. What method do you think they might come up with?

Up and Down Events

Sometimes it is difficult to predict whether or not an event will take place. Other times you know for sure.

1. Use **Student Activity Sheet 1.** Put a check in the column that best describes your confidence that each event will take place.

	Statement	Sure It Won't	Not Sure	Sure It Will
A.	You will have a test in math sometime this year.			
B.	It will rain in your town sometime in the next four days.			
C.	The number of students in your class who can roll their tongues will equal the number of students who cannot.			
D.	You will roll a "7" with a normal number cube.			
E.	In a room of 367 people, two people will have the same birthday.			
F.	New Year's Day will come on the third Monday in January.			
G.	When you toss a coin once, heads will come up.			
H.	If you enter "2 + 2 =" on your calculator, the result will be 4.			

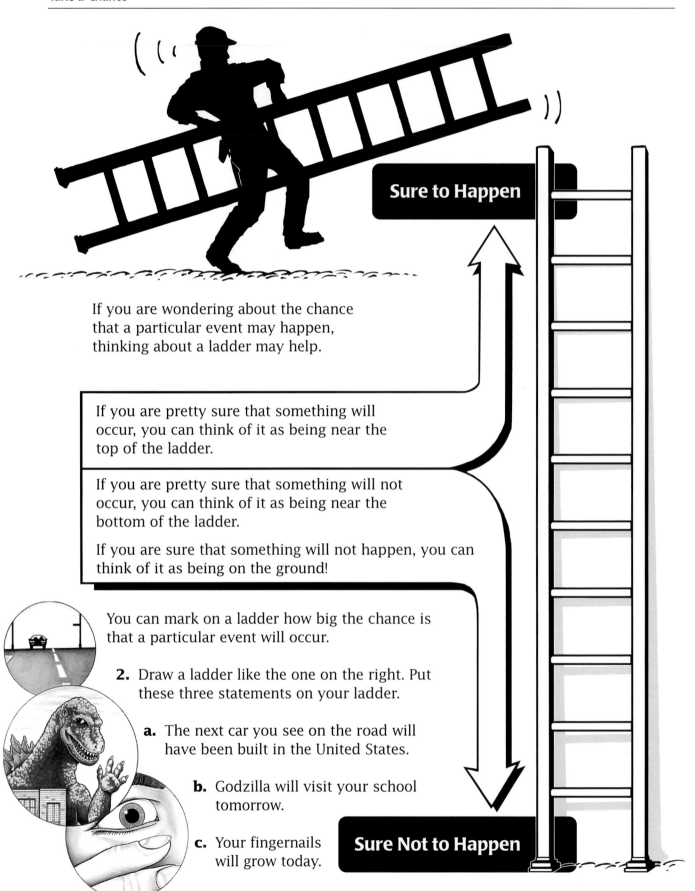

Sure to Happen

If you are wondering about the chance that a particular event may happen, thinking about a ladder may help.

If you are pretty sure that something will occur, you can think of it as being near the top of the ladder.

If you are pretty sure that something will not occur, you can think of it as being near the bottom of the ladder.

If you are sure that something will not happen, you can think of it as being on the ground!

You can mark on a ladder how big the chance is that a particular event will occur.

2. Draw a ladder like the one on the right. Put these three statements on your ladder.

a. The next car you see on the road will have been built in the United States.

b. Godzilla will visit your school tomorrow.

c. Your fingernails will grow today.

Sure Not to Happen

3. Now go back to the table on page 11 and put the statements from the table on one ladder. Explain why you put the statements where you did.

4. Put the following statements about chance on a ladder:
"I'm sure it will happen."   "There's a 50-50 chance."
"That's unlikely."   "It's very likely to happen."
"It probably will."   "There's no way it will occur."
"There's a 100% chance."   "It seems very unlikely."
"There is a 0% chance."   "It could happen."

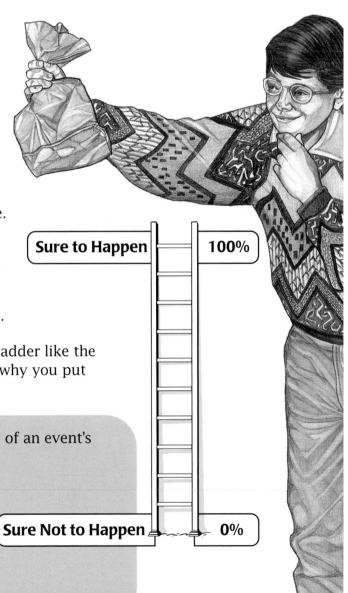

Sure to Happen

Sure Not to Happen

Match 'Em Up

Dan is doing an experiment. He has a bag holding pieces of paper of equal size, numbered 1 to 20. He is going to pick a number from the bag. Here are some possible outcomes for the number he will pick:

    a. It will be even.

    b. It will be divisible by five.

    c. It will be a 1 or a 2.

    d. The digits in the number will add up to 12.

    e. It will be smaller than 16.

Sure to Happen   100%

5. Put the five statements on a ladder like the one on the right and explain why you put them where you did.

Sure Not to Happen   0%

These ladders show that the chance of an event's happening is between 0% and 100%.

- Events you are sure are going to happen will be at the top.

- Events you are not sure about will be somewhere in between.

- Events you are sure will not happen will be at the bottom.

HILLARY IS WALKING TO THE SCIENCE LAB CARRYING HER PET BULLFROG, NEWTON.

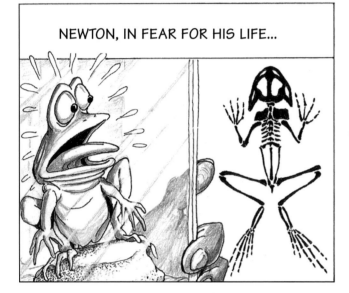

NEWTON, IN FEAR FOR HIS LIFE...

...JUMPS OUT OF HIS AQUARIUM AND HOPS OFF AS FAST AS HIS LITTLE FEET CAN CARRY HIM.

Hillary finally found Newton. He was sitting on this tile: ➡️

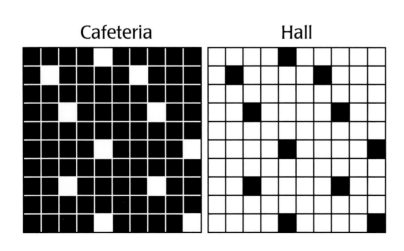

Cafeteria   Hall

6. Look at the two floors on the left. Do you think Hillary found Newton in the cafeteria or the hall? Explain.

7. What if, instead, Newton was sitting on this tile:

Is it likely that he was on the same floor?

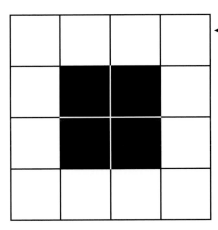

Here is another tiled floor.

Sure to Happen ——— 100%

8. Hillary's frog, Newton, made a dash for freedom on this floor. Draw a scale like the one shown on the right. Mark the chance that Newton would end up on a black square. Explain why you marked the scale where you did.

Sure Not to Happen ——— 0%

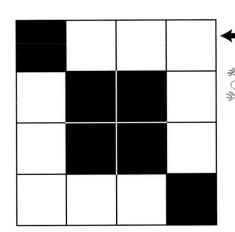

← Now look at another floor.

9. a. Mark the chance that Newton would end up on a black square on this floor on the same ladder that you used for problem **8.**

b. Is it bigger or smaller than the chance in problem **8?** Explain.

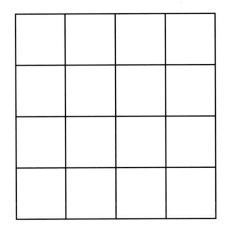

100% ——

10. a. On **Student Activity Sheet 2,** color the first floor so that Newton will have a 50% chance of landing on a black square.

b. Mark the 50% chance on the ladder on **Student Activity Sheet 2.**

0% ——

c. What is another way of saying: "The chance is 50%"?

11. a. For the floor in problem **8,** you can say that the chance of landing on a black square is 4 out of 16. Explain this.

b. Jim says,

THAT'S THE SAME AS 1 OUT OF 4.

Do you agree? Explain.

c. Here is the floor from problem **9.** What is the chance of landing on a black square on this floor?

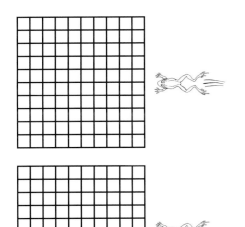

12. a. Color the second floor on **Student Activity Sheet 2** so that Newton's chance of landing on a black square is 1 out of 5.

   b. Now color the third floor on **Student Activity Sheet 2** with any pattern of black and white tiles. What is the chance that Newton will land on a black tile on the floor you made?

13. If you had a black-and-white tile floor, explain how you would find the chance that a frog would land on a black square.

IT TURNED OUT THAT NEWTON DIDN'T HAVE TO WORRY. HE WAS ONLY PART OF AN EXPERIMENT AT THE SCIENCE FAIR ON THE NUMBER OF FLIES FROGS EAT.

Spinners

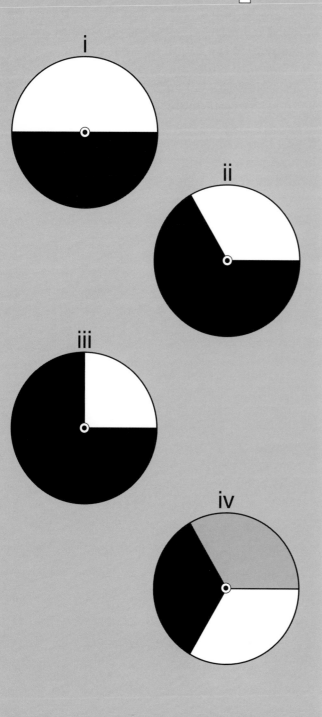

14. Study the spinners on the left.

    a. Can you use spinner i to make fair decisions? Explain your answer.

    b. Can you use spinner ii, iii, or iv to make a fair decision?

    c. Draw a new spinner—different from i, ii, iii, and iv—that can be used to make fair decisions.

15. a. Draw a chance ladder in your notebook. For each spinner on the left, mark the ladder to show the chance of landing in the black part.

    b. Use a method other than a ladder to express the chance of landing in the black part of each spinner.

Jim made this spinner and colored in this floor. Jim says,

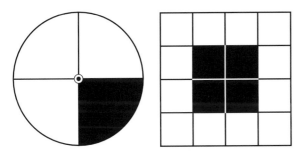

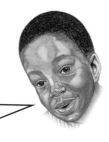

THE SPINNER AND THE FLOOR GIVE THE SAME CHANCE FOR LANDING IN THE BLACK PART.

16. Do you agree with Jim? Explain.

Activity

17. Look in the newspaper for statements about chance. Put these statements on a chance ladder. Bring the ladder to school and explain why you decided to place the statements where you did. Here are some examples to help you.

Baseball Update

Chances for a Run at Division Title Slim

By Mel Bergman
of The Reporter staff

It was no surprise that the Calaway CooCoos' manager Regg Loopendorf refused to give a statement regarding his team's

even though the seri
led to a new definitio
Future chances for a
can only hope that it

and that will return the focus that
and all to brin
world that we can all be
will end
have at o

Cease-Fire May End Soon

UPL
Reports that a new s
attempts to bri
ival fa

Home Buyer's Guide

THIS MAY BE YOUR LAST CHANCE TO BUY A NEW HOME ON SILVER LAKE

Site rating guide ★★★★

LATEST LUXURIOUS LISTINGS

The last twenty homes will go on sale this weekend.

The increase in the number of families wanting to settle in this spectacular area has increased dramatically over the last few weeks. The few

the range of views and the availability of easy access to many of the recreational outlets bring a new meaning to the term "Land of Dreams"

Summary

In this section, you saw different ways of expressing chances. You have seen that the chances on a ladder can be expressed with percents. If you are sure that something will happen, you can say the chance is 100%. If you are sure that it will not happen, the chance is 0%. Chances can also be expressed with fractions. You can make a chance ladder using fractions.

Sure to Happen — 100%

Probably

Sure Not to Happen 0%

Summary Questions

18. a. What fraction would you use to represent a 50-50 chance?

  b. Put some other fractions where they belong on a chance ladder.

Below are some statements about chances. Some of them belong together; they are just different ways of saying the same thing.

19. On **Student Activity Sheet 3,** connect all statements that say the same thing. One example has already been done.

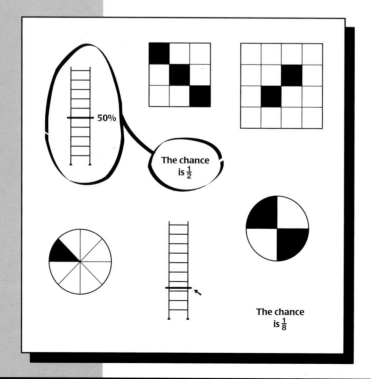

The chance is $\frac{1}{2}$

The chance is $\frac{1}{8}$

JOE FOSS SCHOOL
1200 East 3rd Street
Sioux Falls, SD 57103
(605) 367-4285

Chancy Business

If you roll a number cube one time, the chance that you will roll a 6 is the same as the chance of rolling a 5, a 4, a 3, a 2, or a 1.

1. If you roll a number cube 30 times, about how many times would you expect to roll a 6?

Activity

2. Make a table like the one shown on the right. Roll a number cube 30 times. Tally the number that comes up for each roll.

Number Rolled	Number of Times It Came Up
1	
2	
3	
4	
5	
6	

3. Did what happened differ from what you expected would happen? How?

4. What do you think would happen if you increased the number of rolls to 60?

Nina rolled a number cube. She recorded the results in the table on the right.

Number Rolled	Number of Times It Came Up
1	///
2	ᵀᕼᕇ ᵀᕼᕇ /
3	ᵀᕼᕇ ᵀᕼᕇ
4	ᵀᕼᕇ ᵀᕼᕇ /
5	ᵀᕼᕇ ///
6	ᵀᕼᕇ ᵀᕼᕇ ///

5. a. How many times did Nina roll the number cube?

b. Nina says,

THE CHANCE OF ROLLING A 1 ON THE NEXT ROLL IS GREATER THAN THE CHANCE OF ROLLING A 6.

Do you think that she is right?

6. a. Robert rolled a number cube six times. Do you think that he rolled a 4? Explain.

b. Then Robert rolled the number cube 20 times more. Do you think that he rolled a 4 this time?

Now We're Rolling!

Hillary rolled a number cube many times as part of an experiment.

Number Rolled	1	2	3	4	5
Number of Times It Came Up	44	36	37	41	39

7. Unfortunately, Hillary's pen leaked and covered up the number of times that 6 came up. What do you think is written under the spill? Explain.

Tossing and Turning

During World War II, English mathematician John Kesrich was locked in a cell. He had a coin with him and decided to do an experiment to pass the time. While in the cell, he tossed the coin 10,000 times and recorded the results.

Here is the start of a chart he might have made.

Number of Tosses	Total Number of Heads
1	0
2	0
3	1
4	1
5	2
6	2
7	3
8	3
9	4

8. a. Was the first toss a head?

b. On which toss did the mathematician get heads for the first time?

c. How many tosses did it take to get three heads?

d. How many tails were thrown after eight tosses?

9. About how many heads do you think would come up after 10,000 tosses?

10. How does the percent of heads change as the number of coin tosses increases?

Activity

11. a. If you toss a coin 30 times, how many times do you expect heads to come up?

Toss a coin 30 times. Tally the results in a chart like the one below.

H	T

b. Did your results match what you predicted?

c. Combine your results with those of everyone in the class. How do the class results compare with your individual results?

As you toss a coin many times, the percent of heads approaches 50%, or $\frac{1}{2}$.

On any single toss, though, you cannot tell whether a head or a tail will come up.

Although you cannot predict a single event, if you repeat an experiment many times, a pattern can appear.

Think B4 You Act

Pick a number from 1 to 4 and write it down on a piece of paper.

12. a. If every student in the class writes down one number, how many times do you expect each number to be picked?

b. Count all the 1s, 2s, 3s, and 4s selected and put the information in a table. Look at the results. Is this what you expected? Why or why not?

13. If you were a game show host and wanted to put a prize behind one of four doors, where would you put the prize? Give a reason for your choice.

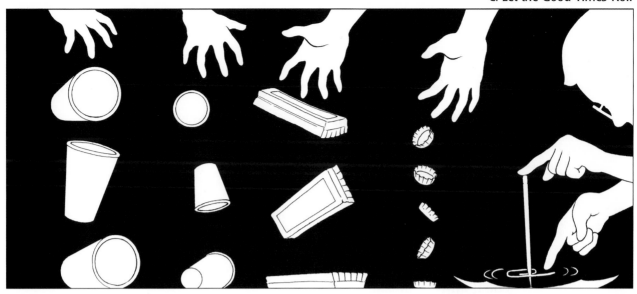

Find the Chance

Back in Section A, problem **19** (page 6), you experimented with these objects:

- a large paper cup

- a small paper cup

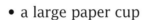

- a chalkboard eraser

- a bottle cap

- the spinner on the left

14. Look again at your work on problem **19**, page 6. Based on the 30 throws for your object, estimate the chance that each possibility will occur when you throw the object.

Mathematics in Context • Take a Chance

25

Summary

You can find the chance of an event by experimenting with many, many **trials.** In the short run, what happens may not be what you expect. But in the long run, your results will get closer and closer to what you expect.

When tossing a coin or rolling a number cube, each new trial will offer the same chances as the previous one. A coin or number cube cannot remember what side it landed on last.

Summary Questions

15. a. If you toss a coin 10 times and get a head every time, what is the chance of getting a head on the 11th toss?

    b. If you roll a number cube over and over again, what do you think will happen to the percent of even numbers that come up as you keep rolling?

16. How many times do you think you have to toss a coin before you can begin to see any patterns in the outcomes?

Families

There are many different types of families. Some families have one adult.

Some families have two adults, and some families have more.

Some families have children, and some do not.

1. **a.** Suppose you look at 20 families with two children. How many of these families do you think will have one boy and one girl?

    b. Other students in your class may not agree with your answer to part **a.** Write a short explanation to help convince them that your answer is correct. Drawing a diagram may be helpful.

girl

boy

2. You can **_simulate_** a study of two-child families by tossing two pennies. A head will represent a girl, and a tail will represent a boy. Toss the two pennies 20 times. See how many families with one boy and one girl you get. Was the result the same as your guess for problem **1a?**

Robert's Clothes

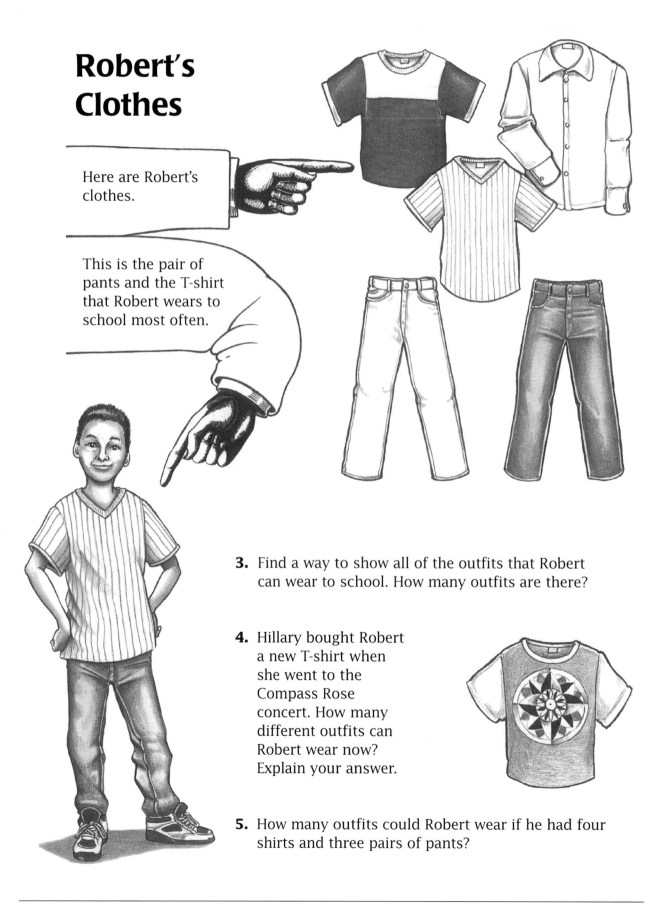

Here are Robert's clothes.

This is the pair of pants and the T-shirt that Robert wears to school most often.

3. Find a way to show all of the outfits that Robert can wear to school. How many outfits are there?

4. Hillary bought Robert a new T-shirt when she went to the Compass Rose concert. How many different outfits can Robert wear now? Explain your answer.

5. How many outfits could Robert wear if he had four shirts and three pairs of pants?

Hillary's Clothes

One day, Hillary decided to choose a shirt and a pair of pants with her eyes closed.

6. What outfit would you expect to see Hillary wearing?

7. How could Hillary have used number cubes to help her choose her clothes?

Hillary says,

> THE CHANCE THAT I WILL PICK MY FROG SHIRT WITH CHECKERED PANTS IS 1 OUT OF 36.

8. Is Hillary right? Explain.

Open or Closed?

If you are with a group of three people, here is a way of choosing one person.

Stand in a circle, facing each other. One of you (or everyone at once) says: "One, two, three . . . go!"

At "go," each person puts out either an open hand or a closed fist.

Hillary, Robert, and Kevin played the game. Each winner is shown on the right in the table below.

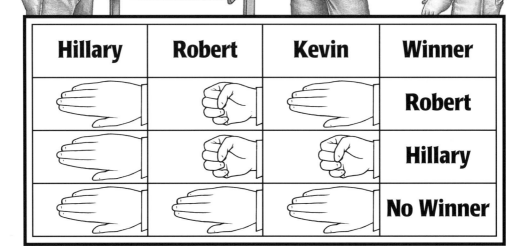

Hillary	Robert	Kevin	Winner
✋	✊	✋	**Robert**
✋	✊	✊	**Hillary**
✋	✋	✋	**No Winner**

9. Describe another situation in which there is no winner if you use this method.

10. How many combinations of open and closed hands are there in the game? List as many as you can.

11. Do you think this is a fair way to decide something? Why or why not?

Mazes

Hillary has a pet mouse named Harry. She is bringing Harry to school today because the class is running mice through mazes for an experiment. The mice are put in at one end of the maze. At the other end, there is food in room 1, 2, 3, or 4. The mice cannot tell (or smell!) which door leads to the food. They, therefore, have an equal chance of going through any of the doors.

This is a top view of the maze that Hillary is using.

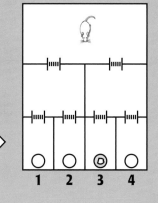

When the students bring all of the mice that they own to school, there are 60 in all.

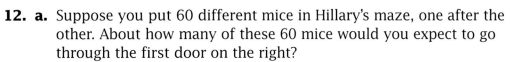

12. a. Suppose you put 60 different mice in Hillary's maze, one after the other. About how many of these 60 mice would you expect to go through the first door on the right?

b. About how many would you expect to end up in room 3, where the food is?

c. Would exactly that many end up in room 3?

d. Is the chance that a mouse will end up in room 3 greater than, less than, or equal to the chance that it will end up in room 2? Why do you think so?

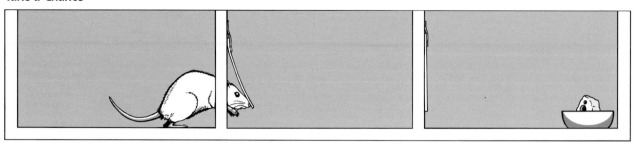

Each mouse has two different choices to make before reaching one of the final rooms. To describe the choices, you can use a picture called a **tree diagram.**

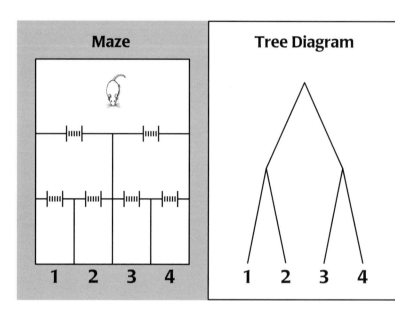

Maze

Tree Diagram

1   2   3   4

1   2   3   4

13. a. Use **Student Activity Sheet 4.** Put an H on the tree diagram at the place Harry would start.

b. If Harry finds the food in room 3, trace Harry's path on the maze.

c. Trace Harry's path on the tree diagram.

Robert wonders how the mice would behave in a different maze.

Another maze is shown on the right. The tree diagram representing the maze is shown below.

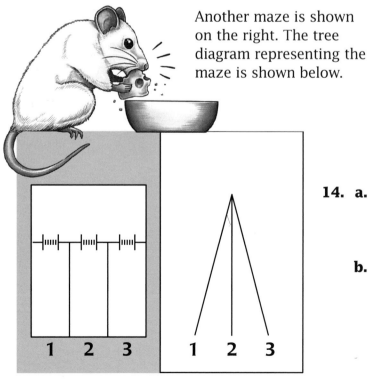

1   2   3

1   2   3

14. a. If you put 60 mice in this maze, about how many would you expect to end up in room 3?

b. What is the chance that a mouse would end up in room 3 for this maze?

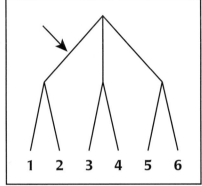

15. Suppose the class puts 60 different mice in a maze that goes with the tree diagram on the left.

  a. About how many of these 60 mice would you expect to take the path that the arrow points to?

  b. About how many would you expect to end up in room 2?

  c. What is the chance that one mouse starting at the beginning will end up in room 2?

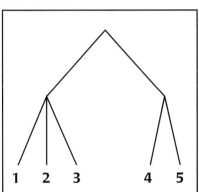

16. a. On the left is a tree diagram for a new maze. About how many of the 60 mice would you expect to end up in each room for this maze?

  b. What is the chance that a mouse would end up in room 3 for this maze?

17. On the left is a tree diagram for a different maze.

  a. What is the chance that a mouse will take the first door on the left? the middle door?

  b. What is the chance that a mouse will end up in room 2? room 3? room 6?

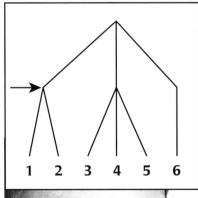

Two Children Again

Tree diagrams can be useful for more than just mice.

Consider families with children once more.

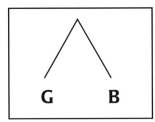

A tree diagram can show the two possibilities for one child.

18. Each path on this tree diagram has an equal chance. What is the chance of having a girl?

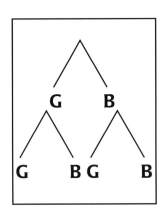

If a family has a second child, you can extend the tree diagram like the one on the left.

19. a. Copy the tree diagram and trace the path for a family that had a girl first and then a boy.

b. What are all the possible combinations for a family with two children?

c. If there are 20 families with two children in Hillary's class, how many would you expect to have two girls? What is the chance that a family will have two girls?

d. Is the chance greater to have two girls or to have a boy and a girl? Explain.

Now look at families that have three children.

20. a. Extend the tree diagram to show a third child.

b. List all of the different possibilities for a family with three children.

c. Robert says, "It's less likely for a family to have three girls than to have two girls and a boy." Explain this statement.

d. Make some other statements using the tree diagram from part **a.**

Activity

Sum It Up

21. Roll two different-colored number cubes. For each pair of numbers that can come up, what are the different sums you can get?

Hillary and Robert sometimes play Sum It Up during lunch.

They each pick one of the possible sums of two number cubes. Then they roll the number cubes, and the first person to roll his or her sum four times wins. The loser has to clean up the other's lunch table.

22. Which sum do you think would be best to pick?

Play the game with the person next to you. If you both want the same number, come up with a fair way to decide who gets the number.

23. Record the sums that are thrown. What was the winning sum in your game?

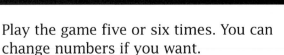

Play the game five or six times. You can change numbers if you want.

24. Now what do you think is the best sum to choose?

	1	2	3	4	5	6
1						
2						
3						
4						
5						
6						

25. Student Activity Sheet 5 has a grid showing the possible numbers for each of two number cubes.

a. For each square, fill in the sum of the numbers.

b. How many different combinations are possible when you roll two number cubes?

c. How many ways can you get a sum of 10 with two number cubes?

d. What is the best number to pick if you are playing Sum It Up? Is your answer different from your choice in problem **24?**

26. a. Draw a tree diagram to show all of the possible combinations for rolling two number cubes. It might be messy!

b. Color the squares in the grid from problem **25** and the paths in the tree diagram from part **a** that give a sum of 10.

27. a. What is the chance of rolling two 1s? What is the chance of rolling doubles?

b. What is the chance of rolling a 7?

28. What do you think is the chance of *not* getting a 10? *not* getting a 7?

Treasure

During a hike along the shoreline at low tide, Hillary and Robert find a big chessboard on the sand.

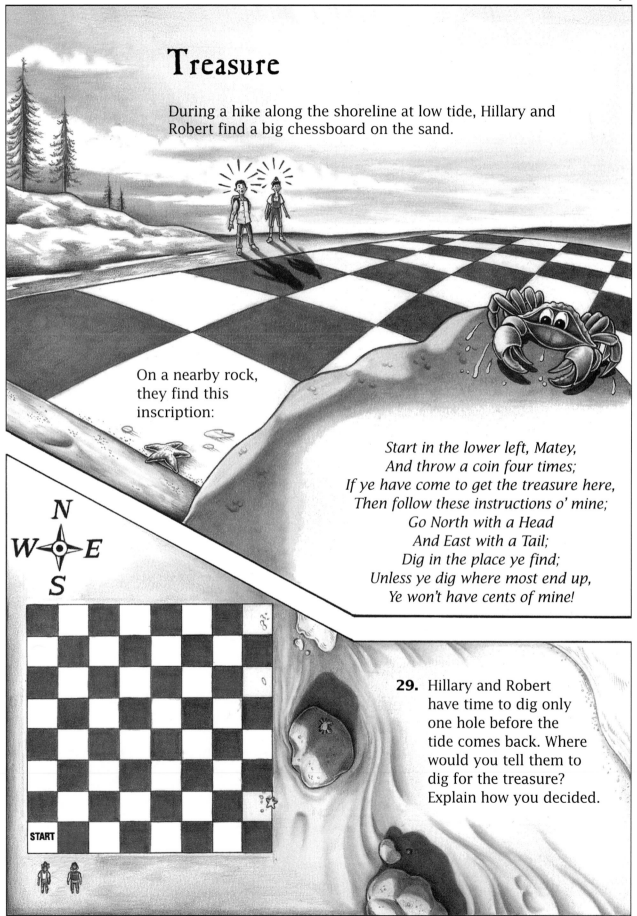

On a nearby rock, they find this inscription:

Start in the lower left, Matey,
And throw a coin four times;
If ye have come to get the treasure here,
Then follow these instructions o' mine;
Go North with a Head
And East with a Tail;
Dig in the place ye find;
Unless ye dig where most end up,
Ye won't have cents of mine!

29. Hillary and Robert have time to dig only one hole before the tide comes back. Where would you tell them to dig for the treasure? Explain how you decided.

START

Summary

In this section, you learned that counting the number of ways an event can occur can help you find the chances of the event.

You can write all of the possible ways that something can occur, or you can draw pictures. Tree diagrams are one type of helpful picture.

A tree diagram can give information about:

• all possible outcomes,

• the chance that any single outcome will occur.

Here is a tree diagram of problem **3** (Robert's clothes) from page 28.

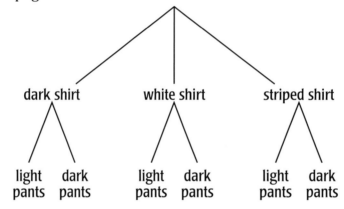

Summary Questions

30. If Robert picks his clothes at random, what is the chance that he will pick a striped shirt and light pants?

31. If a tree diagram ends with eight branches, is the chance of each outcome the same? Give an example to support your answer.

Section A. Fair

1. In your own words, define each of the following terms:

    a. chance

    b. fair

2. Give an example that shows how a coin could be used to do the following:

    a. make a fair decision

    b. make an unfair decision

3. Troy says, "There is a 70% chance of snow today!" Explain what this means.

4. The teacher announces, "Everyone with brown eyes can leave school early today!" Is this a fair decision or not? Explain.

5. Margaret bought five raffle tickets at the Holiday Hip Hop. Suzanne bought three raffle tickets. A total of 210 raffle tickets were sold.

    a. What are Margaret's chances of winning?

    b. What are Suzanne's chances of winning?

    c. Is this raffle fair? Explain.

6. Decide whether or not each event listed below is fair. Explain your decision.

    a. All boys get five pieces of candy, and all girls get four.

    b. All children with brown hair get an "A."

    c. A bag is filled with 10 white marbles and 10 red ones. Without looking, you reach in the bag and grab a marble. If you grab a white one, you can pick a movie for the class to watch.

    d. A bag is filled with 20 white marbles and 10 green ones. Without looking, you reach in the bag and grab a marble. If you grab a green marble, you do not have to take the history test.

Section B. What's the Chance?

1. Draw a ladder like the one on the right. Then put these statements about chance on the ladder:

   a. It will definitely happen.

   b. There is a 25% chance it will happen.

   c. It will not happen.

   d. There is a 0% chance it will happen.

   e. There is a 100% chance it will happen.

2. What number could you use to represent an event that is sure to happen?

3. What number could you use to represent an event that definitely will not happen?

4. What fraction could you use to represent each of the following chances:

   a. a 50% chance

   b. a 25% chance

   c. a 75% chance

5. a. Draw a spinner that can be used to make a fair decision.

   b. Explain why the spinner in part a can be used to make a fair decision.

6. Draw a picture to represent each of the following percents:

   a. 10%

   b. 25%

   c. 50%

   d. 75%

   e. 100%

Section C. Let the Good Times Roll

1. If you roll a number cube, what are your chances of rolling each of the following:

    a. an even number

    b. an odd number

    c. a prime number

    d. a 5

2. In 100 coin tosses, how many times would you expect heads to come up? Explain.

3. In 36 rolls of a number cube, how many times would you expect to roll a 6?

4. **a.** Roll a number cube 36 times and record the results of each roll.

    b. How many times did you roll a 6?

    c. Compare your results for problem **4a** with the predictions you made for problem **3.**

    d. Compare your results for problem **4a** with those of at least two other classmates. Did you get the same results? Why or why not?

5. If you roll a number cube three times and get a 3 every time, what is the chance of getting a 3 on the next roll?

6. If you were to win the lottery once, would that improve your chances of winning again? Explain.

Section D. Let Me Count the Ways

1. In your own words, define the term *tree diagram*.

2. If you have three shirts and three pairs of pants, how many different outfits can you make? Support your answer with a sketch.

3. If you roll two number cubes, what is the chance of rolling each of the following:

    a. pairs

    b. two even numbers

    c. two odd numbers

    d. two numbers that add up to six

    e. two numbers that add up to eight

4. Suppose that your class puts 100 mice in a maze that goes with the tree diagram on the right.

    a. About how many of these mice would you expect to end up in room 3?

    b. What is the chance that one mouse starting at the beginning will end up in room 3?

    c. What is the chance that one mouse starting at the beginning will end up in either room 1 or room 2?

    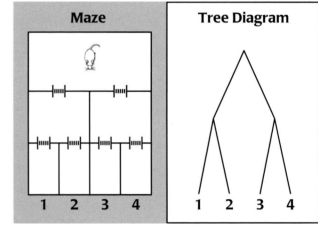

5. Suppose you had a bag of jelly beans that contained:

    > 10 red beans
    >
    > 20 green beans
    >
    > 15 yellow beans
    >
    > 5 purple beans

    a. If you pulled a bean out of the bag without looking, what color bean would you expect to get? Why?

    b. If you pulled a jelly bean out of the bag without looking, what would be your chances of getting a purple one?

CREDITS

Cover

Design by Ralph Paquet/Encyclopædia Britannica Educational Corporation.

Collage by Koorosh Jamalpur/KJ Graphics.

Title Page

Photograph by Robert Drea.

Illustration by Phil Geib/Encyclopædia Britannica Educational Corporation.

Illustrations

1 David Alexovich/Encyclopædia Britannica Educational Corporation; **2** Phil Geib/Encyclopædia Britannica Educational Corporation; **3** Paul Tucker/Encyclopædia Britannica Educational Corporation; **4–6** Phil Geib/Encyclopædia Britannica Educational Corporation; **7** David Alexovich/Encyclopædia Britannica Educational Corporation; **10 (top)** Paul Tucker/Encyclopædia Britannica Educational Corporation; **10 (bottom), 11, 12 (bottom)** Phil Geib/Encyclopædia Britannica Educational Corporation; **12 (top)** Paul Tucker/Encyclopædia Britannica Educational Corporation; **13** Jerome Gordon; **14** David Alexovich/Encyclopædia Britannica Educational Corporation; **16** Jerome Gordon; **17** David Alexovich/Encyclopædia Britannica Educational Corporation; **19** Jerome Gordon; **21–22** Phil Geib/Encyclopædia Britannica Educational Corporation; **23** Paul Tucker/Encyclopædia Britannica Educational Corporation; **25, 27–37,** Phil Geib/Encyclopædia Britannica Educational Corporation.

Photographs

1 © Robert Drea; **8 (top)** © Robert Drea; **8 (bottom)** © Ezz Westphal/Encyclopædia Britannica Educational Corporation; **9 (top)** © Joseph Nettis/Tony Stone Images; **9 (bottom, left and right)** © Robert E. Daemmrich/Tony Stone Images; **11** © Robert Drea; **24–25, 36** © Robert Drea.